Lost in Space

Andrew Dodds

Book Works

'When we dream of space travel, we dream of freedom and beauty, perfection and transcendence; we dream of what we might become.'

Rocket Dreams, How the Space Age Shaped Our Vision of a World Beyond,
Marina Benjamin

'The Future isn't what it used to be.'

July 20, 2019, A Day in the Life of the 21st Century, Arthur C. Clarke

THAT NEIL ARMSTRONG and Buzz Aldrin set foot on the moon on July 20, 1969 has passed into legend. Project Apollo, America's most celebrated contribution to escape velocities, burned as brightly and intensely in the popular imagination as the Saturn V rockets which freed the astronauts from earth's gravity. From 1969 until 1972, glowing like a beacon of progress and exploration, the idea of space travel became a way to make sense of existence, a way to 'fit our small lives into the bigger picture', [1] a way to find form in the void. As one of the most widely documented and viewed events in contemporary history, the *Apollo 11* moon landing seemed to unite humanity for a brief utopian moment in a collective imagining that things might be otherwise. There is a parity between the otherness of space and our internalisation of it, where 'travelling upwards and travelling towards Enlightenment are one and the same thing.' [2] Space travel, our first tentative steps into the cosmos, reflects our 'quest for new horizons and frontiers, for human expansion and even for salvation.' [3] Looking outward, 'outro-spection', rhymes with introspection; experience with expectation; the future with the past.

The moment, July 20, 1969, has become a monument. The events at Tranquillity Base, this promised New Eden where Armstrong and Aldrin as Adam and Eve performed kangaroo jumps and kicked moondust for an audience of millions, are accessible as photographs and videos supplied by NASA. In stark contrast to the burst of speed and energy expended to leave earth's gravity and the abrupt life of Project Apollo, the actual site, the scene of events, will be preserved for millennia. The objects, the footprints, the landscape itself, are all 'vacuum-packed' in an atmosphere 'thinner than the best vacuum we can make in a laboratory' [4] on earth. Barring a massive impact or the intervention of the burgeoning ventures of commercially minded space tourism ('Be prepared to someday see pieces of *Apollo 11* listed for sale on eBay' [5]), the scene will survive for many generations to come. Beyond the ravages of time, like priceless artifacts in a climate controlled anthropological tableau, the objects await re-examination. To use an archaeological analogy, Tranquillity Base can be said to be 'more like Pompeii than Rome.'

This abandoned stage set, Tranquillity Base, has remained untouched and unseen by us for almost four decades: the television camera on the tripod still pointing forlornly at *Eagle*; the lens of the Hasselblad being slowly blinded by space dust; the American flag, toppled during the astronauts ascent from the lunar surface. Yet there are no images of the Apollo Missions taken independently of the programmes themselves. Space exploration has never returned to Project Apollo. The predominant trend in astronomy has been to look ever deeper into space, to the far reaches of time, in attempts at uncovering profound insights about our place in the universe. The *Hubble Space Telescope* continues to detect ever-older star formations in hitherto undiscovered regions of deep space. When attention does turn to the moon the focus is usually to gather geological and chemical data rather than exploring the cultural landscape of space travel.

And so, the moon returns nightly to haunt us like some 'Marie Celestis', carrying the ghosts of our dreams and aspirations. Scattered across its surface, skirting the lunar equator are another five deserted stage sets just like that at Tranquillity Base. Each one is rich with associated artifacts: in The Ocean of Storms the plutonium battery continues to breathe life into the Apollo Lunar Surface Experiments; at Oceanus Procellarum are the golf balls hit by Alan Shepard; at Hadley Rille the hammer and feather that featured in a televised experiment; at Fra Mauro the family photographs of Charles Duke; and at Taurus-Littrow one of the Lunar Roving Vehicles. Though the objects themselves may have succumbed to obsolescence, the dreams and aspirations invested in them have not.

[1] Marina Benjamin, *Rocket Dreams, How the Space Age Shaped Our Vision of a World Beyond*, Vintage, 2004 [2] ibid [3] ibid [4] From correspondence with Alan Aylward, Head of Atmospheric Physics Laboratory, University College London [5] P.J. Capelotti, *Space, the Final [Archaeological] Frontier*, Archaeology.org, 2004

THE APOLLO 11 MISSION accomplished the basic objective of the Apollo program; that is landing two men on the lunar surface and returning them safely to earth. Crew members for this historic mission were Neil A. Armstrong, Commander; Michael Collins, Command Module Pilot; and Edwin E. Aldrin, Jr., Lunar Module Pilot.

The *Apollo 11* space vehicle was launched from Kennedy Space Center Launch Complex 39A on July 16, 1969, at 08:32:00 a.m. e.s.t. (13:32:00 GMT). The spacecraft and S-IVB stage of the launch vehicle were inserted into a 100.7- by 99.2-mile earth parking orbit. After a 2-½ hour checkout period, the spacecraft/S-IVB stage combination was injected into the translunar coast phase of the mission. Trajectory parameters after the translunar injection firing were nearly perfect. A midcourse correction of 20.9 feet per second was made during the translunar phase. During the remaining periods of free attitude flight, passive thermal control was used to maintain spacecraft temperatures within desired limits. The Commander and the Lunar Module Pilot transferred to the lunar module during the translunar phase to make the initial inspection and preparations for the systems checks that would be made shortly after lunar-orbit insertion.

The docked spacecraft were inserted into a 60- by 169.7-mile lunar orbit at approximately 76 hours after launch. Four hours later, the lunar-orbit circularisation maneuver was performed to place the combined spacecraft in a 65.7- by 53.8-mile lunar orbit. The Lunar Module Pilot entered the lunar module at approximately 81 hours after launch for initial powerup and systems checks. After a planned sleep period was completed at 93-½ hours elapsed time, the lunar module crewmen transferred to the lunar module and made final preparations for descent to the lunar surface. The lunar module was undocked from the command and service module at a mission time of approximately 100 hours. The lunar module descent orbit insertion maneuver was performed with the descent propulsion system at 101-½ hours into the mission, and the powered descent initiation occurred 1 hour later. The lunar module maneuvered manually approximately 1100 feet down range from the preplanned landing point during the final 2-½ minutes of descent.

Man first landed on the moon at 03:17 p.m. e.s.t. on July 20, 1969, 102 hours 45 minutes 39.9 seconds mission elapsed time. The spacecraft landed in Mare Tranquillitatis (Sea of Tranquillity) at latitude 0°41'15" N. and longitude 23°26' E. based upon the coordinates of reference 2-15. After a 2-hour postlanding checkout of all the lunar module systems, the crew configured the spacecraft controls for lunar stay and ate their first meal on the lunar surface. A crew rest period had been planned to precede the extravehicular activity of exploring the lunar surface but was not needed. After donning the back-mounted portable life support and oxygen purge systems the Commander egressed through the forward hatch and deployed an equipment module from the descent stage. A camera in the equipment module provided live television coverage of the Commander as he descended the ladder to the surface. The Commander made first contact at 09:56:15 p.m. e.s.t. on July 20, 1969, or 109 hours 56 minutes 15 seconds into the mission. The Lunar Module Pilot egressed soon thereafter, and both crewmen used the initial period on the surface to become acclimated to the reduced gravity and the unfamiliar surface conditions. A contingency soil sample was taken from the surface, and the television camera was deployed to include most of the lunar module in the field of view. Figure 2-15 is a photograph of the Commander as he stood beside the deployed United States flag during this part of the extravehicular activity. The crew then activated scientific experiments which included a solar wind detector, a passive seismometer, and a laser retroreflector. The Lunar Module Pilot evaluated his ability to operate and move about, and he was able to do so rapidly and confidently. The crew collected approximately 21 kilograms of lunar surface material for analysis. The surface exploration was concluded in the allotted time of 2-½ hours, and the crewmen reentered the lunar module at a mission time of 111-½ hours.

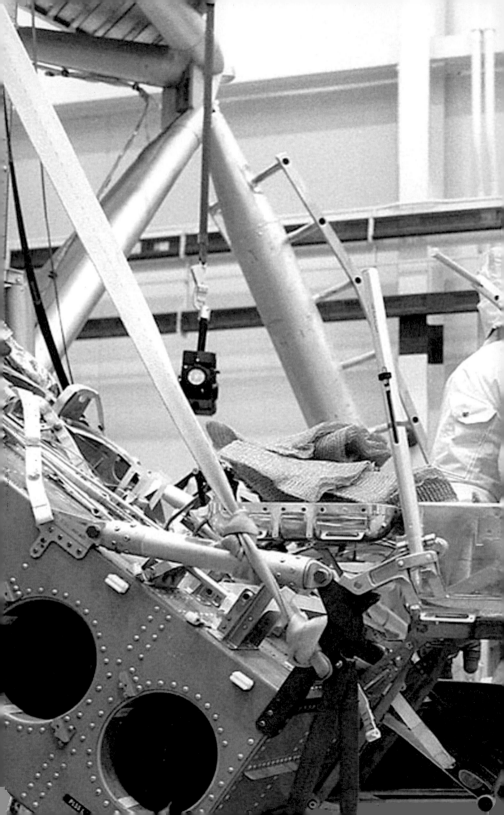

After a rest period, ascent preparation was conducted and the ascent stage lifted off the surface at 124-¼ hours from earth launch. A nominal firing of the ascent engine placed the vehicle into a 45- by 9-mile orbit. After a rendezvous sequence similar to that performed on *Apollo 10*, the two spacecraft were docked at the mission time of 128 hours. After transfer of the crew and samples to the command and service module, the ascent stage was jettisoned, and the command and service module was prepared for transearth injection.

The return flight started with a 150-second firing of the service propulsion engine during the 31st lunar revolution at 135-½ hours into the mission. As in translunar flight, only one midcourse correction was required, and passive thermal control was exercised for most of the transearth coast. Because of inclement weather in the planned recovery area, the landing point was moved 215 miles down range. The service module was separated from the command module 15 minutes before reaching the entry interface altitude of 400,000 feet. Following an automatic entry sequence and landing system deployment, the command module landed in the Pacific Ocean after a flight duration of 189 hours 18 minutes 35 seconds. The landing coordinates, as determined from the spacecraft computer, were latitude 13°19' N. and longitude 169°9' W.

After landing, the crew donned biological isolation garments; they were then retrieved by helicopter and taken to the primary recovery ship, the *U.S.S. Hornet*. The crew and lunar material samples were placed in a mobile quarantine facility for transport to the Lunar Receiving Laboratory in Houston.

All spacecraft systems performed satisfactorily and, with the completion of the *Apollo 11* mission, the national objective of landing men on the moon and returning them safely to earth, before the end of the decade, was accomplished.

Apollo Program Summary Report, pages 36 and 38, NASA, 1975

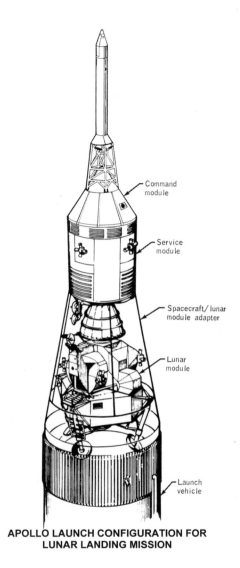

Command module

Service module

Spacecraft/lunar module adapter

Lunar module

Launch vehicle

**APOLLO LAUNCH CONFIGURATION FOR
LUNAR LANDING MISSION**

The Lunar Module (LM) separates from the Command Service Module (CSM) and descends to the moon's surface while the CSM remains in lunar orbit. When the astronauts have completed lunar activities the LM Ascent Stage is launched from the LM Descent Stage to rendezvous with the CSM. The LM Descent Stage remains on the lunar surface. When the astronauts have transferred from the LM Ascent Stage to the CSM the Ascent Stage is jettisoned into lunar orbit, eventually to impact with the moon.

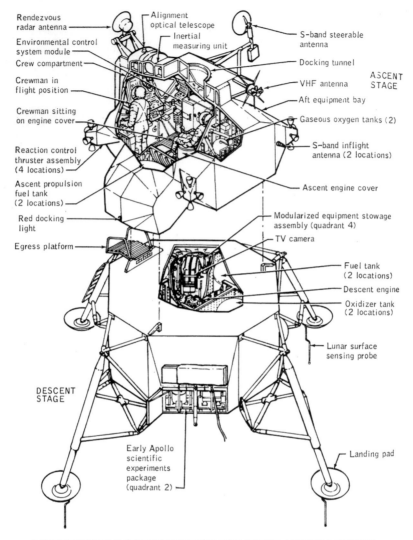

Rendezvous radar antenna

Environmental control system module

Crew compartment

Crewman in flight position

Crewman sitting on engine cover

Reaction control thruster assembly (4 locations)

Ascent propulsion fuel tank (2 locations)

Red docking light

Egress platform

Alignment optical telescope

Inertial measuring unit

S-band steerable antenna

Docking tunnel

ASCENT STAGE

VHF antenna

Aft equipment bay

Gaseous oxygen tanks (2)

S-band inflight antenna (2 locations)

Ascent engine cover

Modularized equipment stowage assembly (quadrant 4)

TV camera

Fuel tank (2 locations)

Descent engine

Oxidizer tank (2 locations)

Lunar surface sensing probe

DESCENT STAGE

Early Apollo scientific experiments package (quadrant 2)

Landing pad

LUNAR MODULE CONFIGURATION FOR INITIAL LUNAR LANDING

The crash sites of the Lunar Module Ascent Stages from *Apollos 12, 14, 15* and *17* are 3.94 S, 21.20 W; 3.42 S, 19.67 W; 26.36 N, 0.25 E; 19.96 N, 30.50 E respectively. The crash sites of *Eagle* and *Orion*, the *Apollo 11* and *16* Lunar Modules, are unknown.

LUNAR MODULE ASCENT STAGE

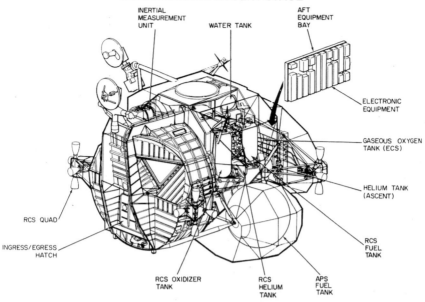

INERTIAL MEASUREMENT UNIT

WATER TANK

AFT EQUIPMENT BAY

ELECTRONIC EQUIPMENT

GASEOUS OXYGEN TANK (ECS)

HELIUM TANK (ASCENT)

RCS QUAD

INGRESS/EGRESS HATCH

RCS FUEL TANK

RCS OXIDIZER TANK

RCS HELIUM TANK

APS FUEL TANK

LUNAR MODULE DESCENT STAGE

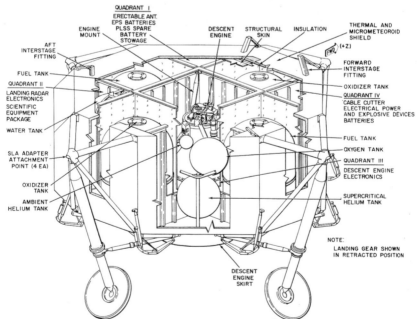

QUADRANT I
ERECTABLE ANT.
EPS BATTERIES
PLSS SPARE BATTERY STOWAGE

ENGINE MOUNT

DESCENT ENGINE

STRUCTURAL SKIN

INSULATION

THERMAL AND MICROMETEOROID SHIELD

(+Z)

AFT INTERSTAGE FITTING

FORWARD INTERSTAGE FITTING

FUEL TANK

QUADRANT II

OXIDIZER TANK

LANDING RADAR ELECTRONICS

QUADRANT IV
CABLE CUTTER
ELECTRICAL POWER AND EXPLOSIVE DEVICES BATTERIES

SCIENTIFIC EQUIPMENT PACKAGE

WATER TANK

FUEL TANK

OXYGEN TANK

SLA ADAPTER ATTACHMENT POINT (4 EA)

QUADRANT III
DESCENT ENGINE ELECTRONICS

OXIDIZER TANK

SUPERCRITICAL HELIUM TANK

AMBIENT HELIUM TANK

NOTE:
LANDING GEAR SHOWN IN RETRACTED POSITION

DESCENT ENGINE SKIRT

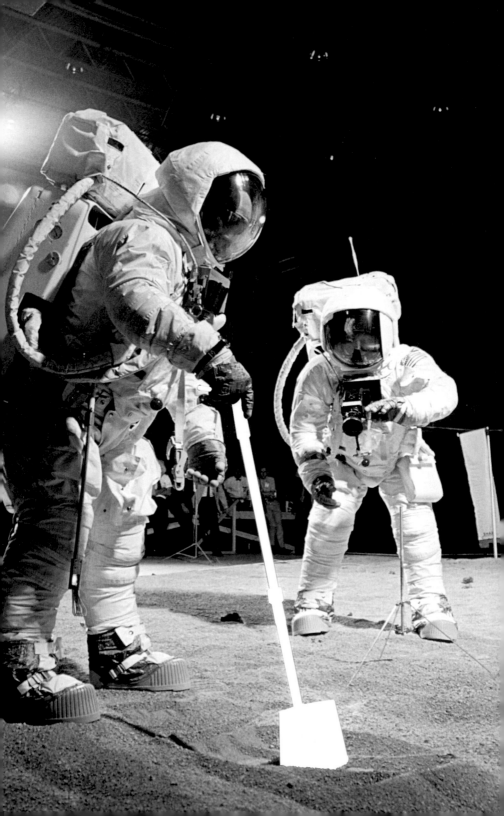

01. **Antenna, S-Band** (1)
02. Apollo Space Boots (Aldrin), Model A7L (2)
03. Apollo Space Boots (Armstrong), Model A7L (2)
04. Apollo Space Suit (Aldrin), Model A7L (1)
05. Apollo Space Suit (Armstrong), Model A7L (1)
06. Armrests (4)
07. Bag, Deployment, Life Line (1)
08. Bag, Deployment, Lunar Equipment Conveyor (1)
09. Bag, Emisis (4)
10. Bag, Lunar Equipment Conveyor & Waist Tether (1)
11. **Bag, Lunar Equipment Transfer** (1)
12. **Bulk Sample Scoop** (1)
13. Cable, S-Band Antenna (1)
14. Camera, Hasselblad El Data (1)
15. Canister, Environmental Control System (Lithium Hydroxide) (2)
16. Capsule, Aluminium, small (1) Contains Commemorative Items
    21, 40, 49, 51
17. Central Station (1)
18. Commemorative Plaque attached to the Lunar Module Descent Leg (1)
19. Container Assembly, Disposal (1)
20. Container, Portable Life Support System Condensate (1)
21. Contingency Lunar Sample Return Container, Handle (1)
22. **Core Tube Bits** (2)
23. Defecation Collection Device (4)
24. Document Sample Box, seal (1)
25. Environmental Control System, Canister (1)
26. Environmental Control System, Bracket (1)
27. Environmental Sample Containers, "O" rings (2+)
28. Extension Handle (1)

29. Film Magazines (2+)
30. Filter, Oxygen Bacterial (1)
31. Filter, Polarizing (1)
32. Flag, United States of America, 3' x 5' (1)
33. Food Assembly, Lunar Module (4 man days) (1)
34. Food Bags, empty (2+)
35. **Gnomon (excluding mount)** (1)
36. Gold Replica of an Olive Branch (1)
37. **Hammer** (1)
38. Hasselblad Pack (1)
39. Insulating Blanket
40. Kit, Electric Waist, Tether (1)
41. **Laser Ranging Retroreflector** (1)
42. Life Line (1)
43. Lunar Equipment Conveyor (1)
44. Lunar Equipment Conveyor Assembly (1)
45. **Lunar Module Descent Stage** (1)
46. Lunar Surface Stereoscopic Close-up Camera (1)
47. Medals Commemorating Two Dead Cosmonauts (2)
48. Modular Equipment Storage Assembly, Bracket (1)
49. Mission Patch from Apollo I (1)
50. Oxygen Purge System, Brackets (2+)
51. Overshoes, Lunar (2)
52. Pallet Assembly #1 (1)
53. Pallet Assembly #2 (1)
54. **Passive Seismic Experiment Package** (1)
55. Plastic Covering for Flag (1)
56. Pressure Garment Assembly, Gas Connector Covers (2)
57. Primary Structure Assembly (1)

58. Remote Control Unit (Portable Life Support System) (2)
59. Retaining Pins for Flag and Staff Storage (2+)
60. Sample Return Container/Oxygen Purge System, Adapter (2)
61. Sample Return Container, Seal Protectors (2)
62. Scongs (1)
63. Silicon Disc carrying statements from Presidents Nixon, Johnson, Kennedy, Eisenhower, and from leaders of 73 other nations (1)
64. Small Scoop (1)
65. Solar Wind Composition Staff (1)
66. Solar Wind Composition Bag (1)
67. **Spring Scales** (2)
68. Stainless Steel Cover, Commemorative Plaque (1)
69. Storage Container (empty) (1)
70. Stowage Compartment, left hand side (1)
71. Television Cable Assembly, 100ft (1)
72. Television Camera (1)
73. Television Camera Handle/Cable Assembly Cord (1)
74. Television Camera Lens, Lunar Day (1)
75. Television Camera Lens, Wide Angle (1)
76. Television Subsystem, Lunar (1)
77. Tether, Waist, Extravehicular Activity (4)
78. Tongs (1)
79. Trenching Tool (1)
80. Tripod (1)
81. Tube, 8ft Aluminium (1)
82. Urine Collection Assembly, large (2)
83. Urine Collection Assembly, small (2)
84. York Mesh Packing Material (1)

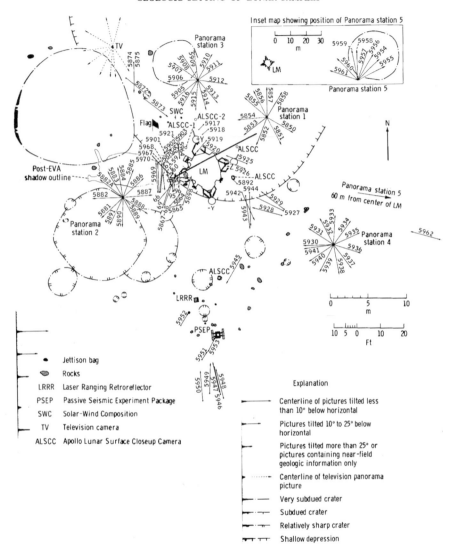

FIGURE 3-15. — Preliminary map of EVA photographs and television pictures taken at the landing site.

CORRESPONDENCE WITH DR ALAN AYLWARD, Head of Atmospheric Physics Laboratory, University College London

Can you please outline the moon's atmospheric conditions?

There is very little 'atmosphere'. Most gases are not held on to long enough to form any sort of layer around the moon. It does have an atmosphere of sorts – but it depends how you define atmosphere. We have a collaborating group in Boston who image the Sodium 'halo' around the moon – that is, it is surrounded by a thin 'atmosphere' of Sodium atoms. But that is defining 'atmosphere' as something that is thick enough and detectable enough that you can image it. It is not an atmosphere as YOU would define it – or even most scientists. It is so thin, it is thinner than the best vacuum we can make in a laboratory. It is so thin you are dealing with individual molecules moving on ballistic trajectories and not interacting, rather than a fluid as we would expect most 'atmospheres' to be. It is only marginally denser than the interplanetary medium.

Given that our terrestrial telescopes can view 'detailed' images of objects on the edges of our solar system, is it possible to view objects the size of, for example, an American flag (dimensions 3 x 5ft) on the lunar surface with these telescopes? Can you please outline the main difficulties there may be in doing so?

I will have to go away and do some calculations of the resolving power of the big 8 and 10 metre telescopes to be sure but my guess is that they should be able to 'detect' the flag (i.e. say there is 'something' there) but they won't be able to resolve it (you won't see the stars and stripes.)

The telescope on *Mars Express* is much smaller than the biggest ground-based telescopes we have and it can make out a smudge on the surface which is thought to be *Beagle* – so that gives you some idea what we can see. If you want me to turn these arm-waving statements into properly worked out numbers I can...

Is it possible for satellite telescopes such as *Hubble* to view an object the size of, for example, an American flag (dimensions 3 x 5ft) on the moon? Can you please outline the main difficulties there may be in doing so?

It's the same with *Hubble* – yes it can 'see' quite small objects on the moon but whether you can tell WHAT they are would need detailed calculations. *Hubble* is not that much better than the best ground-based telescopes. It is smaller but doesn't have to look through the atmosphere. The ground-based telescopes get around the atmospheric distortion by using special techniques called adaptive optics which enables them to see as well as *Hubble* under the best circumstances. I guess the question comes down to what you want to do. Do you want to 'spot' it – that is detect the 'splodge' on the surface where it is – or do you want to be able to count the stars in the flag?

The difficulty is nearly all in the resolving power of the telescope. If it's big enough it will be able to do it. Do you want me to calculate what I think is the smallest resolvable object? As I say, you'd have to say what you mean by resolution. I vaguely remember them looking in the past for objects on the moon – but it may have been something big like the Lunar Lander left by the Apollo missions or one of the Surveyor landers.

In relation to the questions above, please do the calculations and if possible, relate them to particular telescopes e.g. say, the three most powerful optical telescopes. I'd like to know what it is likely/theoretically possible for them to resolve?

OK, I have done the calcs and it's actually worse than I thought. The *Hubble* telescope (which is a 2.4m telescope) could resolve no better than about 120 metres at the distance of the moon in visible light. You do better with a bigger telescope – the biggest available at the moment on the ground is the *Keck* which has a 10 metre aperture. This could resolve down to about 23m, so it wouldn't even properly see the lunar module let alone the flag. You can get better resolution by going to the ultraviolet – if you looked at 50nm

wavelength instead of 500nm (which is the visible) you could get the 23m down to 2.3 metre, which is getting near the resolution you want, but unfortunately you can't see UV light of that wavelength from the ground as it is stopped by the upper atmosphere. So you either have to wait for them to build the OWL (OverWhelmingly Large telescope) with an aperture of 100m or fly a 10m telescope with UV capability. (Actually telescopes never actually work to their diffraction limit so even this would not do.) If you want to resolve the stars on the flag you would need an unfeasibly large telescope – 10,000m diameter at least.

I stress these are physical limits set by the physical properties of light – you can't get around them by boosting the signal or anything. I am using what is known as the diffraction limit of the telescope – that says the best resolving power of the telescope is 1.22lambda/d where lambda is the wavelength you are viewing in and d is the diameter of the telescope. If lambda and d are in metres then the resolving power is in radians (approx 57 degrees to a radian). This is the minimum angle at which you can differentiate two objects.

I spent ages on this, this afternoon, because I couldn't work out how *Hubble* could have imaged Pluto on these figures as it should just about be able to resolve the distance between Pluto and Charon, its satellite, yet I know I have seen hazy images of the disk. I found out later they had looked at Pluto in UV light which gave them the extra resolving power. It was pretty marginal though.

I've been trying to discover if there are known images of the objects taken by any means other than those of the Apollo missions themselves. You mentioned a vague recollection of a previous search for objects on the moon: if you can remember what the outcome of this was I'd be grateful.

My memory of this must be faulty. I thought they tried looking for the crash residue of the Ranger spacecraft and whether they could see the Surveyor spacecraft but in the first case they must have been hoping for rather a large scorched patch, and in the latter it must have been one of the orbiters they were using to search for it, not ground-based earth telescopes which they would have realised had no chance.

I am undertaking research on the artifacts left behind on the moon by the Apollo space missions.

I know that *SMART-1* is currently in lunar orbit and that it has optical imaging equipment onboard. I am writing to ask if this equipment is capable of detecting items such as the US flag, lunar rover etc. that remain on the lunar surface?

I have just talked about this with the *SMART-1* Project Manager, and he asked me to give you the following answer. Even though we shall cover virtually the whole moon with our observations by several instruments on *SMART-1*, unfortunately we will not be able to image the landing sites with enough resolution to detect the presence of the Apollo Lunar Rovers or any other remains from the Apollo missions.

We believe that a resolution of about 1 metre would be necessary for that. *SMART-1* has a camera with a resolution of 0.005176°, which translates into a resolution of about 90 metres from 1000km altitude. In order to image the Apollo remains with our camera, we would then need to fly at about 11km altitude which is not really feasible. The *SMART-1* spacecraft will be able to fly in a lower orbit, because of the amount of spare fuel which is now available, after its very successful and efficient journey, but not that low! Instead, the optics of our camera were designed for the specific scientific needs of this mission. We could have easily designed an optical system with a narrower field of view and capable of detecting the Apollo remains, but alas this was not a mission goal.

I am interested in how the artifacts on the lunar surface might look now given the atmospheric conditions of the moon and their length of exposure to it. Can I ask you to describe how you imagine the objects might look? For example, the condition of the paint on the craft; the deterioration of the nylon flag; is there a covering of dust; might they have shifted from their original position; is it likely the footprints are being slowly eradicated etc.? Plus anything else you want to add.

It is unlikely they are shifted. The only thing that can destroy them is the heat/cold cycle (which may for example split off paint from surfaces) and micrometeoroids which over millions of years will perforate them and reduce them to dust. Over the 40 years they have been on the moon I doubt they have more dust on than when they were left (the biggest dust flux having been kicked up by the astronauts jumping about.) I can't tell you how well the paint job is holding up. I don't know how much stuff was painted – a lot of it will have been vapour-deposit coated and that will be a bit more resistant. The people to ask would be NASA engineers who know about the coatings. I have seen solar arrays that have been returned to earth from orbit and although they are known to have meteor strikes on them (and some are big splatter zones and therefore obvious) much of the damage is microscopic and to the naked eye much of it looks pristine still.

Dr Alan Aylward, Head of Atmospheric Physics Laboratory,
University College London

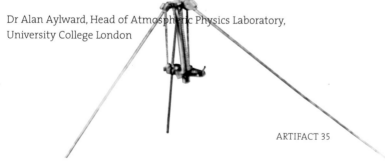

ARTIFACT 35

My guess is that the spacecraft would be suffering from marginal deterioration from the effects of radiation (darkening of various components, as was noted by the *Apollo 12* astronauts at the Surveyor site), as well as possible dust coverings, but these may be the effect of the descent stage disruptions of the surface when the LMs were landing/taking off. The footprints are thought to be as near to permanent as one can get, short of a meteorite hitting them. And don't forget that the wreck of the LM ascent stage is somewhere up there, crashed after it was abandoned. I would imagine that this looks like a car crash, only much more interesting! No one has seen this site, because it is not known exactly where the ascent stage crashed. An artistic representation of this crash, as far as I am aware, would be unique.

Dr P.J. Capelotti, writer and Senior Lecturer in Anthropology and American Studies, Penn State University

I think it is unlikely that there will be currently much dust on the Apollo artifacts, except perhaps that uplifted by the various spacecraft during launch from the lunar surface. With no lunar atmosphere, metal tarnishing should be at a minimum.
The extreme temperature fluctuation from day to night will probably cause some expansion and contraction of the metal, affecting the paint.

Footprints will probably endure for hundreds, if not thousands, of millions of years. They will be very slowly eradicated by the impact of small meteorites. Of course, they could be obliterated in an instant by a direct strike from a large meteorite.

John McFarland, Armagh Planetarium

ARTIFACT 67

It depends on the material of the artifact. There is no wind on the moon but there is both extremes of hot and cold and solar winds and radiation and impacts from debris entering the moon's surface so these forces would affect the artifacts left there.

Conrad and Bean on *Apollo 12* landed near the *Surveyor 3* crash landing and took some notes, removed some parts of the *Surveyor* and took them back as the first archaeological artifacts from the moon. I don't know about pictures from this mission. As far as I know there are no other pictures of *Apollo 11* site or other lunar sites taken by later missions. We have the technology right now to take pictures and archaeologically map all lunar sites but it has never been done to the best of my knowledge. Space heritage still has not received the publicity and interest that it justifies.

Dr Beth O'Leary, Lecturer in Anthropology, New Mexico State University

ARTIFACT 12

Probably the UV light from the Sun will cause the most deterioration. Not sure what happens to nylon, but probably the flag will be damaged. It is unlikely there is a coating of dust.

The footprints are probably still there – I think eradication would be an extremely slow process – most of the damage to footprints would be from dust/blast when the lander blasted off to return to Earth, so there would be damage and destruction close to the bottom part (left behind) of the lander, but further away, the footprints should be in good shape. Rubber seals would probably be destroyed by the UV. Metal would be mostly OK.

Not sure what the tyres of the moon buggy were made from – if rubber, then they would have four flats by now! Basically, I think plastics would be damaged, metals OK, natural (e.g. rubber) materials destroyed.

ARTIFACT 37

Richard Wainscoat, University of Hawaii, Institute for Astronomy

II. Summary and Conclusions

N. L. Nickle and W. F. Carroll

The successful return of the Surveyor 3 hardware, lunar soil, and photographs taken by the Apollo 12 astronauts permitted 36 studies to be made by more than 80 investigators.

Chapter III contains the significant engineering results obtained from these studies. Chapters IV through XI contain the results of the scientific investigations. Because the papers were written individually by members of the investigating teams and therefore are presented in a different format than are chapters I through III, some redundancy or differences in interpretation may occur.

This chapter is a summary of the engineering and scientific results derived from the investigations.

Engineering Results

Results of the engineering investigations were essentially "nonspectacular"; the primary value lies in the fact that no failures or serious adverse environment effects on the hardware were uncovered that, to some degree, had not been anticipated. The absence of detected major effects and the resulting implications for future space vehicles are significant. However, the absence of effects should not be construed to indicate that the problems associated with material and component selections, test, design, assembly, and systems test can be ignored.

Spacecraft Changes

Measured reflectance data have been analyzed in order to separate and understand the effects of lunar dust and radiation damage. The radiation-induced discoloration on various surfaces was found to be proportional to the degree of solar illumination, and is in reasonable agreement with laboratory simulations. The discoloration was found to be subject to photo-induced oxygen bleaching. This bleaching was responsible for a considerable change in color during the several months of exposure since return to Earth. Organic contamination is not a significant factor in the observed discoloration of the external surfaces.

Almost all exposed surfaces on the camera were partially covered with a fine layer of lunar dust. Substantial variations existed in the quantity and apparent particle size of dust on the various surfaces. The dust distribution indicates that the fines were disturbed and implanted upon the spacecraft primarily by the initial Surveyor landing and by the approach and landing of the Apollo 12 Lunar Module (LM). The presence of dust, even in very small quantities, can have a significant effect on temperature control and optical performance of hardware on the lunar surface.

Lunar dust adhering to the camera's optical filters consists of less than 1- to 40-μm-wide particles of calcic plagioclase, clinopyroxene, tridymite, and glass. Most particulates are complex mixtures of more than one crystalline phase and not micrometer-sized pieces of single-phase minerals. The assumed parent material of this dust is a fine-grained breccia or a soil from such a rock type.

Dust on the camera's mirror consists of particles large enough to see with the unaided eye (contaminants consisting of gypsum, calcite, and beta-cloth fibers) and fine-grained angular fragments. Spherical particles are restricted primarily to the smaller size ranges; about 1 percent of the particles is spherical at 0.7-μm diameter compared with 10 percent at less than 0.2-μm diameter. Ninety percent of the total mass is within the size range of 0.3 to 3 μm. Very few lunar particles larger than 4 μm exist; some of these may be aggregates.

Sources of the dust on the mirror, and thus also of many other surfaces, include that disturbed by the abnormal Surveyor landing and by manipulations of the surface sampler scoop. It has been demonstrated that more dust exists now than at the time of the Surveyor 3 mission. Thus, the approach of the LM and/or natural lunar transport processes contributed additional material to the mirror's optical surface.

Spectral reflectance, gonioreflectance, spectral transmission, and ellipsometry measurements conducted on various components of the camera indicate that the following changes occurred on the lunar surface:

(1) A nonparticulate coating of unknown composition and origin was deposited on the mirror and possibly other surfaces. The coating is insoluble in acetone and benzene. Tests are continuing in an attempt to identify the coating.

(2) The thickness of the nonparticulate coating is not uniform, and is estimated as approximately one-half wavelength ($\lambda = 550$ nm).

(3) One or more particulate layers were deposited by at least two of the following events:
  (a) Abnormal landing of Surveyor 3.
  (b) Manipulation of the surface sampler scoop.
  (c) Normal transport processes.
  (d) Approach and landing of the LM.
  (e) Redistribution and/or contamination during camera retrieval and return.

(4) Distribution of dust on all surfaces is not of uniform thickness.

(5) Increase in spectral transmission of the blue and green filters may be due to partial dissipation of the Inconel coating.

(6) Dust on the filters caused a 25-percent decrease in transmission.

(7) Radiation darkening caused a decrease in transmission of the clear filter.

(8) Mirror acquired a pit density of approximately 1 pit per 2 mm² on cleaned areas.

The exterior camera surfaces showed discoloration patterns produced by lunar surface particles that were eroded and entrained on Surveyor by the LM exhaust during landing. The particles

were ejected almost horizontally at 40 m sec⁻¹, struck the camera, and partially whitened its already dusty and radiation darkened surface.

Exterior surfaces of the scoop were discolored by the presence of lunar soil, but most prominently discolored by exposure to solar radiation on the Moon. The degree of discoloration, which was made apparent by a change of the original light blue paint to a whitish blue, depended upon the duration and angle of surface exposure to the Sun. Adhesion of lunar soil varied with the type of surface. Lunar material adheres more readily, in order, to (1) painted surfaces (approximately 10⁴ dyne cm⁻²), (2) Teflon, and (3) metallic surfaces (10³ to 10⁴ dyne cm⁻²).

The Surveyor spacecraft moved from its landed configuration sometime between May 1967 and November 1969. It is conjectured that the movement occurred as a result of a sudden failure of the leg 3 shock absorber. The movement at footpad 2 was in the amount of 5° of tilt and 7 to 8 cm of lateral translation in the form of a rotation about footpad 1, which was embedded in the lunar soil.

Organic Contamination Analysis

Determination of the presence of organic contaminants was considered important in order to understand the discoloration process and to help identify possible sources of contaminating gas. Parts of the mirror and exterior camera surfaces were washed with solvents, and the residues were analyzed. Major components of the extract residue from the mirror was dioctyl phthalate and silicone oil. LM descent engine products are evident only in trace amounts.

Extracts were taken from the middle shroud on the side facing the LM and the side away from the LM. Major constituents found are hydrocarbons, dioctyl phthalate, and silicones. Several other species, thought to be derived from the Surveyor 3 vernier engine exhaust, were observed. The LM descent engine products are twice as abundant in the leeward sample; this difference in abundance is believed due to erosion of the side facing the LM by entrained lunar dust particles.

Sources of the various organic contaminants are hydrocarbons from lubricating or vacuum pump oils and general terrestrial contamination, silicones from sources as oils, outgassing of electronics and plasticizers, copolymer of vinyl alcohol and styrene from electronics insulation, and nitrogenous compounds from LM and possibly Surveyor 3 engine exhaust. The organic contamination levels do not contribute significantly to the discoloration of the various surfaces. Analyses for organic contaminants and identification of their sources, even if low in concentration, should be recognized as an important criterion for the design of optical or other active instruments for future spacecraft.

Micrometeorite Impact Analyses

A major effort in the analysis of Surveyor 3 parts has been the search for hypervelocity impact features—an effort roughly analogous to the search for the needle in the haystack. A great number of low-velocity features exist that were caused by lunar particles striking the surfaces due to Surveyor and Apollo landing events, handling of the material, and natural phenomena. The 1- to 4.5-μm size of the surface features prohibited the effective use of optical instruments. However, all participating investigators concluded that no material or surface features were found that definitely could be stated to be meteoritic in origin. Consequently, determinations of the flux rate of hypervelocity particles at the Surveyor 3 site were based on the absence of diagnostic features; as such, the flux rates represent upper limits only. In each instance, the determinations were in general agreement with those obtained from Pioneers 8 and 9, Cosmos 163, Pegasus satellites, and others.

The optical filters were inspected for primary impacts with the same results. However, because of the spatial orientation of the filters, the well-defined field of view of space for each filter and the nature of their finish provided an excellent opportunity to determine an implied impact rate of secondary particles. Particles 1 μm and larger with velocities high enough to produce plastic flow in glass were found to be about 10^3 times the cratering rate expected for primary micrometeoroids. The rate is approximately 800 impacts cm^{-2} yr^{-1} (2π sterad)$^{-1}$ for impacts ≥ 1 μm.

Comparison of pictures of the lunar surface taken 31 months apart by Surveyor 3 and Apollo 12 show no meteorite craters ≥ 1.5 mm in diameter.

Radioactivity and Radiation Damage Analyses

The camera visor was examined for an alpha radioactive deposit formed by the decay of radon isotopes diffusing from the lunar surface. The conclusion reached is that the gross activity on the visor is due to the activity of the paint. However, the amount of ^{210}Po activity expected on 1 cm^2 of the lunar surface after an infinite time at Oceanus Procellarum was estimated to be $(0.88 \pm 4.43) \times 10^{-3}$ disintegrations sec^{-1} cm^{-2}.

The cosmogenic radionuclide ^{22}Na was measured in painted and unpainted aluminum tubes, camera support collars, brackets, scoop, soil removed from the scoop, and in the mirror. The average galactic cosmic-ray flux incident on Surveyor 3 was about 4 ± 1 protons cm^{-2} sec^{-1}. Detailed radionuclide production rate calculations based on satellite data of solar flares were used to estimate the contribution of solar flare protons to the total ^{22}Na produced in Surveyor 3. Galactic cosmic-ray production of ^{22}Na in aluminum derived from the Lost City meteorite agrees with the galactic cosmic-ray production rate in Surveyor 3, indicating almost identical cosmic-ray fluxes at 1 AU and at 2.35 AU. The ^{26}Al and ^{22}Na content of lunar soil recovered from the Surveyor 3 scoop indicates that the soil originated from an average depth of 3.5 cm in the lunar surface.

The tritium content of painted aluminum samples removed from the camera shrouds was measured to be 0.48 ± 0.005 dpm cm^{-2}. This activity is more than a factor of 3 larger than would be expected if it had received the same average cosmic-ray flux and solar flux as the top of Apollo 12 lunar rock 12002. It is thought that an excess of tritium existed which was due to artificial contamination; there was a correlation, however, of tritium content with exposure to sunlight, indicative of solar wind tritium.

There was no evidence of microstructure effects caused by particle bombardment from the solar wind, solar flares, or cosmic radiation. The size and appearance of precipitate particles of Mg$_2$Si indicate appreciable thermal aging (which possibly occurred during fabrication). Elevated lunar temperatures may have been sufficient to result in thermal diffusion of trapped solar wind He and Ne in a high density of dislocations occurring to a depth of 10 μm.

Solar Wind Rare Gas Analysis

The polished aluminum tube contained trapped solar wind He and Ne with a ^{4}He-to-^{20}Ne ratio of 295. This value is lower than the ratios measured from the Apollo 11 and 12 solar wind composition (SWC) experiments. This could be due to ^{4}He diffusion loss or to a small residual dust contamination. The ^{4}He distribution around the aluminum tube is in agreement with the theoretically expected distribution and corresponds to an average solar wind ^{4}He flux of 7 × 10^6 cm^{-2} sec^{-1}. If ^{4}He diffusion loss had occurred, the average ^{4}He flux could be as high as 13 × 10^6 cm^{-2} sec^{-1}. Neglecting the small influence of possible dust contamination or of diffusion loss, table 1 shows the average isotopic composition for the solar wind during exposure of Surveyor 3 material and the Apollo 11 and 12 SWC experiments. Compared with the Apollo 11 and 12 results, the ratio of ^{4}He to ^{3}He is unexpectedly high. The differences may reflect time variations in the composition of the solar wind.

Particle Track Analyses

The energy spectrum of iron-group solar cosmic-ray particles was determined for the first time over the energy range 1 to 100 MeV/nucleon using the optical filter glass. The difference between the observed spectrum and the limiting spectrum derived previously from tracks in lunar rocks gives an erosion rate of 0 to 3 Å/yr. High-energy fission of Pb, induced by galactic cosmic-ray protons and alpha particles, was observed.

Soil Property Analyses

The soil sample returned in the scoop provided a unique opportunity to evaluate earlier, remotely controlled, in-situ measurements of lunar surface bearing properties. Assuming the lunar regolith at Surveyor 3 has a bulk density of 1.6 g cm^{-3} at 2.5-cm depth, then the agreement is good. The bearing capacity varied from 0.02 to 0.04 N cm^{-2} at bulk densities of 1.15 g cm^{-3} to 30 to 100 N cm^{-2} at 1.9 g cm^{-3}.

TABLE 1.—*Average isotopic compositions for the solar wind during exposure of Surveyor 3 material and Apollo 11 and 12 SWC experiments*

Ratio	Surveyor 3	Apollo 11	Apollo 12
^{4}He:^{3}He	2700 ±130	1860 ±140	2450 ±100
^{20}Ne:^{22}Ne	13.3±0.4	13.5±1.0	13.1±0.6
^{22}Ne:^{21}Ne	21 ±5	....	26 ±12

Pictures taken by the Surveyor 3 television camera and photographs by the Apollo 12 astronauts of identical areas have provided the opportunity to evaluate changes in the lunar regolith during the 31 months, and have helped to dispel the impression that the lunar soil may have a thin surface "crust" that breaks into flat "tiles." The impression of "tiles" and "crusting" is an illusion. Rather, the lunar soil deforms and cracks in the same manner as homogeneous, isotropic terrestrial soils of moderate bulk density, with a small amount of cohesion. Photographs viewed stereographically clearly show the three-dimensional character of the disturbed material. No changes in the lunar soil that can be attributed to natural processes have been identified.

A previously unreported feature of lunar fines is the existence of filamentary whisker-like objects attached to individual particles in a manner resembling sea urchins. Twenty particles were found on the red optical filter with whiskers averaging 10 μm long and 0.1 μm wide. It is hypothesized that these whiskers grew on the particles during impact events on the lunar surface. If this explanation is correct, then determination of the fraction of lunar particles that contain whiskers may allow setting limits to theories that predict migration of dust over the lunar surface by various processes. These features presumably have not been observed before because of their friability.

Microbe Survival Analyses

A bacterium, *Streptococcus mitis*, was isolated from a sample of foam taken from the interior of the camera. Available data suggest that the bacterium was deposited in the camera before launch. Lyophilizing conditions existing during pre-launch vacuum tests and later on the lunar surface may have been instrumental in the survival of the microorganism.

A piece of electrical cabling also was subjected to microbiological analysis with negative results. The absence of viable microorganisms could be due to natural dieaway and dieoff caused by vacuum and heat.

Conclusions

The analyses presented and discussed in more detail in chapters IV through XI may be credited with the following achievements:

(1) Collection of a wealth of technical information applicable to the design and fabrication of future spacecraft.

(2) General agreement in the upper limit of micrometeoroid fluxes on the Moon for primary particles less than 1 μm to several millimeters in diameter and larger with values from other sources.

(3) Establishment of the sources and types of organic contamination from Surveyor and Apollo.

(4) Establishment of an almost identical cosmic-ray flux at 1 and 2.35 AU.

(5) An indication of a varying isotopic composition for the solar wind with time.

(6) Discovery of a new active erosion process on the lunar surface.

(7) Discovery of "whiskers" on lunar dust particles.

(8) Demonstration of the ability of a bacterium species to survive the rigors of the lunar environment.

Although the return of additional general hardware from the Moon or from space under similar conditions does not appear to be warranted, specific items (i.e., solar cells) or equipment from specific environments (i.e., high-energy radiation environments, the asteroid belt, etc.) could be valuable. Possible future return of space hardware should be accomplished in a controlled manner in order to preserve the effects of exposure to be examined. The value of scientific investigations on engineering hardware is severely limited by the lack of suitable controls, standards, or documentation of initial conditions. The size, shape, surface texture, and composition of engineering hardware is selected for functional performance, and therefore does not lend itself to scientific analyses. Engineering materials are typically selected for minimum response or change due to environmental factors and are therefore usually less than optimum subjects for evaluation.

In order to accommodate scientists in the future with material suitable for analysis, it is recommended that a set of coupons consisting of different types of material of interest be placed on all spacecraft regardless of the present intent of obtaining or revisiting the spacecraft. Such devices presently exist that are light in weight (several kilograms), have replaceable coupons, can be remotely deployed, and are inexpensive.

Program Objectives

Gemini Program was conceived aft...
...ficials that an intermed...
...ry and the...

NASA
FACTS

S...

The first job performed by th...
American astronauts to the...

This mission was accomplished with the launchin...
6, 1969, of the sixth Sa... ...initial quota
es provided by the Mar... ...nter a...
ctors. The nine rem... ...her exploration of...
...aturn V pro...
orbit.

Marina Benjamin, *Rockets Dreams, How the Space Age Shaped Our Vision of a World Beyond*, Vintage, 2004

Richard Panek, *Seeing and Believing; How the Telescope Opened Our Eyes and Minds to the Heavens*, Viking, 1998

Arthur C. Clarke, *July 20, 2019, A Day in the Life of the 21st Century*, Grafton, 1987

Sources/Further Reading

Frederic Jameson, 'Progress Versus Utopia; or Can We Imagine the Future', from *Art After Modernism*, ed. Brian Wallis, Godine, 1984

Olesya Turkina & Victor Mazin, *In Between Space and Cosmos*, Cabinet, issue 14, 2004

P.J. Capelotti, *Space the Final [Archaeological] Frontier*, Archaeology.org, 2004

Mike Toner, *Some Archaeologists see 'Space Junk' as Treasure*, The Atlanta Journal-Constitution, 2003

Albert J. Derr, *Photography Equipment and Techniques, A Survey of NASA Development*, Technology Utilization Office, NASA, 1972

Apollo Program Summary Report, NASA, 1975

Acknowledgements

Images (pages 2, 7, 10–11, 13-16, 20-22, 25, 29-34) courtesy NASA. All images taken on earth during rehearsals for *Apollo 11* mission.

Inventory based on a list compiled by the Lunar Legacy Project, New Mexico State University.

Pages 34-39 from *Analysis of Surveyor 3 Material and Photographs Returned by Apollo 12*, Chapter 2, 'Summary and Conclusions', NASA Scientific and Technical Information Office, 1972

Thanks to Beth Laura O'Leary and Ralph Gibson of the Lunar Legacy Project, Alan Aylward, P.J. Capelotti, John McFarland, Carl Walker and Richard Wainscoat for their contributions.

Lost in Space

Andrew Dodds

Published and distributed by Book Works
19 Holywell Row, London EC2A 4JB
www.bookworks.org.uk

ISBN 1 870699 76 9

Chap Books: Number 4
Design by Valle Walkley
Printed by B.A.S. Printers, Salisbury

Book Works is funded by Arts Council England